# 101 Turkey Jokes And Riddles

By Stephanie Calmenson
Illustrated by George Wildman

**Weekly Reader Books**
MIDDLETOWN, CONNECTICUT

Publishing, Executive, and Editorial Offices:
Weekly Reader Books
Field Publications
Middletown, CT 06457

What kind of key won't open a door?
A turkey.

What happened to the turkey who swallowed
  a flashlight?
He hiccuped with delight.

1

Why did the turkey get his mouth washed out
   with soap?
Because he was using fowl language.

Joe: I can lift a turkey with one hand.
Sue: I don't believe you.
Joe: Get me a turkey with one hand and I'll
   show you.

When is a turkey like a cute little bunny rabbit?
When he's wearing his cute little bunny rabbit
suit.

Kate: What's the difference between a turkey
and a mattababy?
Jim: What's a mattababy?
Kate: Why, nothing. What's the matter with
you?

If you saw nine turkeys walking down the
street wearing plaid socks and one turkey
walking down the street wearing polka-
dotted socks, what would that prove?
That nine out of ten turkeys wear plaid socks.

What do you call a dirty turkey crossing the road
twice?
A dirty double-crosser.

**Aunt Mabel:** Just look at this turkey! One leg is
longer than the other.
**Uncle Moe:** Were you planning to eat it or
dance with it?

4

Why did they fire the turkey from the
   basketball team?
Too many fowl plays.

Why did the turkey wear red suspenders?
His blue ones were at the laundry.

Why did they let the turkey join the band?
He had the drumsticks.

Why did the turkey cross the road?
It was the chicken's day off.

Turkey: I know a secret.
Pig: Will you tell it to me?
Turkey: No way. You'd just squeal.

What is smarter than a talking turkey?
A spelling bee.

What day was it when the scientist crossed a
turkey with a vampire?
Fangsgiving Day.

Can a turkey have a neck that is 12 inches long?
No, then it would be a foot.

What looks like half a turkey?
The other half.

On which side does a turkey have the most
  feathers?
The outside.

Eddie: If a chicken and a half laid an egg and a half in a day and a half, how long would it take a turkey to sit on a lamppost and hatch a light bulb?
Christina: I give up.
Eddie: So did she!

What has eight legs, six eyes, and feathers?
A man riding a horse and carrying a turkey.

In what month do turkeys gobble the least?
February. It's the shortest month.

Tom Turkey (to friend with bandaged wing): How
 did you hurt yourself?
Injured Friend: See those steps over there?
Tom Turkey: Yes.
Injured Friend: Well, I didn't.

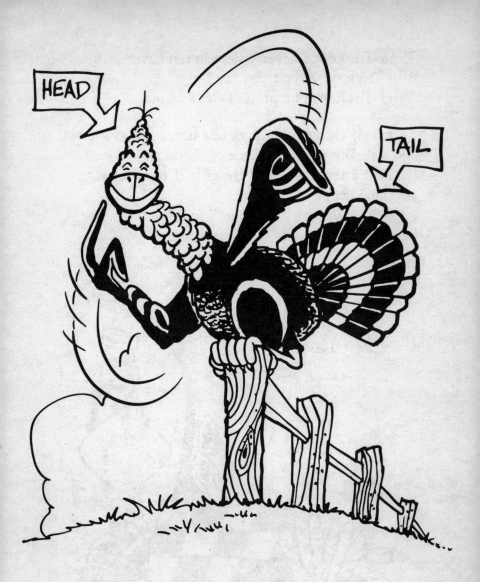

How is a turkey sitting on a fence like a penny?
Head's on one side, tail's on the other.

Two turkeys were looking up to the sky at a passing
jet when one declared, "I could fly like that, too, if
my tail were on fire."

11

**Tina Turkey:** I haven't slept in ten days.
**Sue Turkey:** Aren't you tired?
**Tina Turkey:** Not at all. I sleep nights.

Walking through the park one day, a girl saw a boy and a turkey playing a game of checkers.

"That's amazing!" said the girl. "I've never seen anything like it!"

"He's really not so amazing," said the boy. "I've beaten him three out of five games already."

**Farmer:** How can you do so many strange things in one day?
**Turkey:** I get up early.

**Visitor:** Is Ballpoint really the name of your turkey?
**Farmer:** No, that's just his pen name.

Bob Turkey: I think I need glasses.
Al Turkey: Why?
Bob Turkey: I can't see a thing in the dark.

Clem Turkey: I didn't sleep at all last night.
Clyde Turkey: Why not?
Clem Turkey: I made a mistake and plugged the
electric blanket into the toaster. I kept popping out
of bed all night.

**Lil Turkey:** I wish I had been born in the Dark Ages.

**Jill Turkey:** So do I. You look terrible in the light.

**Mother Turkey:** Why is your brother crying?

**Boy Turkey:** Because I'm eating my corn and won't give him any.

**Mother Turkey:** Is his corn gone?

**Boy Turkey:** Yes. He cried when I ate that, too.

**Waiter:** Have you tried the turkey, sir?
**Diner:** Yes, and I found it guilty.

**Scientist Turkey:** Do you know there are little bugs on the surface of the moon?
**Student Turkey:** What are they called?
**Scientist Turkey:** Lunar-ticks.

**Helen Turkey:** How did you get a ticket to the rodeo?
**Jason Turkey:** It's my sister's ticket.
**Helen Turkey:** Where's your sister?
**Jason Turkey:** Home, looking for her ticket.

**Father Turkey:** Have you been reading those horse stories again?

**Son:** Yes, Dad.

**Father Turkey:** That's why you're having nightmares.

**Turkey:** I don't know what's happening to me. I can't remember anything for more than a few minutes.

**Veterinarian:** How long has this been going on?

**Turkey:** How long has what been going on?

**Uncle Turkey:** This is the perfect spot for a picnic.

**Aunt Turkey:** It must be. Thousands of insects can't be wrong.

**Ralph Turkey:** I was on television today.

**Rita Turkey:** For how long?

**Ralph Turkey:** Until the farmer came home and chased me off it.

**Roy Turkey:** Did you hear about the turkey in the hospital?

**Ray Turkey:** No, what happened?

**Roy Turkey:** He got run down by a steamroller.

**Ray Turkey:** Can we visit him?

**Roy Turkey:** Yes. He's in rooms seven, eight, and nine.

Why did the boy put sun-tan lotion on the turkey?
Because he liked dark meat.

**Jack Turkey:** I had the radio on last night.
**Mac Turkey:** Oh, really. Was it a good fit?

**Boy Turkey:** Have your eyes ever been checked?
**Girl Turkey:** No, they've always been brown.

Richard Turkey: Do you feel like a can of soda?
Daniel Turkey: Why, no. Do I look like one?

Bill Turkey: Have you seen me on television?
Phil Turkey: Oh, sure, I've seen you off and on.
Bill Turkey: How did you like me?
Phil Turkey: Off.

Cindy Turkey: I hear you have a new baby. What's
  her name?
Mindy Turkey: We don't know. She won't tell us.

A man bought a turkey that could speak five languages. He paid one thousand dollars for it. When he got home, he left the turkey with his wife and went out to buy a few things. When he returned home, the turkey was gone.

"Where is my turkey?" asked the man.

"He's in the oven," replied the woman.

"In the oven!" said the man. "But that turkey could speak five languages!"

"Well, then," asked the woman, "why didn't he speak up?"

**Girl Turkey** (whispering in Boy Turkey's ear): A little bird told me you were going to give me a present.

**Boy Turkey:** That bird must have been a cuckoo.

First Turkey: Someone in this barn thinks he's an owl.
Second Turkey: Who?

A baby turkey was kneeling by her bed saying her prayers when her mother said, "I can't hear you."
The baby turkey answered, "I wasn't talking to you."

A turkey was deciding whether or not it was time to eat his dinner. His wife asked, "It's hard for you to make up your mind, isn't it?"

The turkey replied, "Well, yes...and no."

A farmer went to the post office to pick up his mail. "Any mail for Mike Howe (my cow)?" he asked.

"No. But there's a letter here for your turkey," the postman replied.

A turkey was standing in the middle of a busy crossroad when a policeman came by. The turkey asked, "Can you tell me how to get to the hospital?"

The policeman answered, "Sure. Keep standing right where you are."

Pete Turkey: Did you hear the joke about the roof?
Paul Turkey: No.
Pete Turkey: Never mind. It's over your head.

**Maine Turkey:** The winters here are so cold that the farmer has to heat the cows before he milks them.

**Louisiana Turkey:** That's nothing. Our summers are so hot, the farmer has to chill the chickens so they won't lay hard-boiled eggs.

**Stanley Turkey:** Boy, that farmer sure is mean!

**Ollie Turkey:** Why do you say that?

**Stanley Turkey:** I've been watching him pull the ears off the corn.

A turkey was sitting on a fence reading a book. Every so often he would tear out a page, fold it neatly, and sit on it.

"What are you doing?" asked a goat.

"I'm keeping the lions away," said the turkey.

"I don't see any lions," said the goat.

"See how well it works?" said the turkey.

**Baby Turkey:** Mommy, what's a twip?
**Mother Turkey:** A twip is a wide on a twain.

Walt Turkey: I have a cousin in Alaska.
Willie Turkey: Nome?
Walt Turkey: Of course I know him. He's my
 cousin.

Turkey Wife: What did you do all day, dear?
Turkey Husband: I spent hours in front of the
 mirror admiring myself. Is that vain?
Turkey Wife: No, it's nuts.

A hen and a turkey were walking down the road when they came to a restaurant. There were two specials on the menu: Eggs Benedict and Turkey Salad.

"Look at that—Eggs Benedict!" said the hen. "That makes me proud."

"Easy for you to say," said the turkey. "You just have to make a donation. When they serve turkey salad, I'm through."

What two countries can you eat?
Turkey and Chile.

**Sarah Turkey:** See those sheep? It takes five of them to make a sweater.
**Clara Turkey:** I didn't know they could knit.

**Driver:** I'm sorry I ran over your turkey. I'll replace it.
**Farmer:** You can't. You don't have feathers.

Ben Turkey: How would you like it if I gave you a cow and two ducks for your birthday?

Jane Turkey: That would be great. I love milk and quackers.

Two turkeys were standing in the garden.

Zeke Turkey: Hey, do you want to hear a secret?

Zack Turkey: You'd better wait till we go inside. The corn has ears, the potatoes have eyes, and the beanstalk.

Two turkeys were having a conversation when a goat came along. "We'd better continue our talk later," said one of the turkeys. "We won't be able to get a word in edgewise once that goat starts butting in."

When can ten turkeys stand under an umbrella
   without getting wet?
When it isn't raining.

What does a turkey do when she's being chased by
    lions?
The turkey trot.

Who is never hungry at Thanksgiving?
The turkey, because it's always stuffed.

When do turkeys have eight legs?
When there are four of them.

What do turkeys have that no other bird has?
Baby turkeys.

Once there was a turkey who was so smart that the farmer sent him to college. When the turkey came home for the summer, he admitted that he had not done very well in science or history. "But I did really well in foreign languages," the turkey said proudly.

"Really?" asked the farmer. "Say something to me in another language."

"Meow," said the turkey.

Cow: Why are you sleeping under that old truck?
Turkey: So I can wake up oily in the morning.

Horse: Have you ever had an accident?
Turkey: No.
Horse: Never?
Turkey: Well, once I was out in a field and a bull
  butted me straight over a fence.
Horse: That sounds like an accident to me.
Turkey: It wasn't. The bull did it on purpose.

35

A cowhand was riding his horse when he saw a turkey running across the road.

"Hi!" said the turkey.

"Hi!" answered the surprised cowhand. "I didn't know turkeys could talk."

That's when his horse shook his head and said, "You learn something new every day, don't you?"

**Shady Lane Turkey:** The scarecrow on our farm this year is so real-looking, it scared off every single crow.

**Red Roost Turkey:** That's nothing. The scarecrow on our farm is so scary, the crows brought back all the corn they stole last year.

Farmer: What are you doing?
Turkey: I'm writing a letter to myself.
Farmer: What does it say?
Turkey: I don't know. I won't get it until tomorrow.

Ben Turkey: Can you tell me what time it is? I was invited to a barnyard dance and my watch isn't going.
Hilda Turkey: Why? Wasn't your watch invited?

Turkey: Did you hear about the turtle out on the highway?

Sheep: What was a turtle doing on the highway?

Turkey: About one mile an hour.

Kathy Turkey: Darling, I can't leave you.

Kevin Turkey (blushing): Do you really like me that much?

Kathy Turkey: No. But you're standing on my foot.

Sam Turkey: My sister ate a frog.
Sophie Turkey: Did it make her sick?
Sam Turkey: Sick! She could croak at any minute!

A mother turkey was scolding her children. "You bad children," she said. "If your father could see you now, he would turn over in his gravy."

Veterinarians say that one out of every four turkeys is crazy. So, turkeys, check your friends—if three of them seem all right, you're the one.

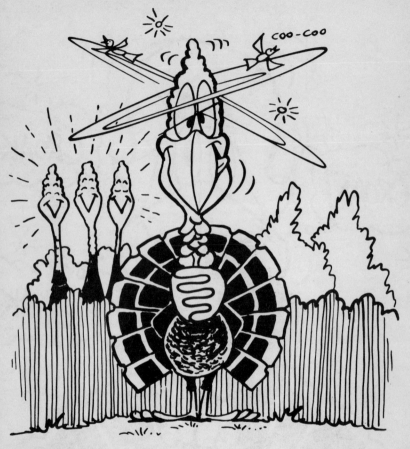

Turkey: I just swallowed a bone.
Cow: Are you choking?
Turkey: No, I'm serious.

Goat: What kind of leather makes the best shoes?
Turkey: I don't know, but banana peels make the best slippers.

Knock, knock!
Who's there?
A very small turkey who can't reach the bell.

A woman opened her refrigerator and found a
turkey lying on a shelf inside.
"What are you doing in my refrigerator?" asked the
woman.
"Isn't this a Westinghouse?" asked the turkey.
"Yes, it is," said the woman.
"Well," said the turkey, "I'm westing."

41

Rick Turkey: What do you dream about at night?
Rock Turkey: Baseball.
Rick Turkey: Don't you dream about anything else?
Rock Turkey: What, and miss my turn at bat?

Musical Turkey: How should I clean my tuba?
Farmer: Try a tuba toothpaste.

**Molly Turkey:** How do you get down from a horse?

**Wally Turkey:** Jump?

**Molly Turkey:** Nope.

**Wally Turkey:** Use a ladder?

**Molly Turkey:** Nope.

**Wally Turkey:** Well, how *do* you get down from a horse?

**Molly Turkey:** You don't get down from a horse, you get down from a goose.

**Michael Turkey:** On our farm, a hen laid an egg six inches long.

**Jessie Turkey:** Big deal. We can beat that on our farm.

**Michael Turkey:** How so?

**Jessie Turkey:** With an egg beater.

**Rosie Turkey:** I feel like a cup of tea.

**Terry Turkey:** Funny, you don't look like one.

**Rosie Turkey:** What I meant was, would you join me in a cup of tea?

**Terry Turkey:** Do you think there'll be room for both of us?

**Rosie Turkey:** No, silly. Now tell me, Terry, what hand do you use to stir your tea with?

**Terry Turkey:** My right hand.

**Rosie Turkey:** Shame on you! Next time use your spoon!

What do you do with a blue turkey?
Cheer him up.

When is a turkey like a ghost?
When he's a-gobblin'.

Crow: Wanna fly?
Turkey: Sure.
Crow: Wait a minute and I'll catch one for you.

Mrs. Turkey: What's the difference between a
   cabbage and a lemon?
Mr. Turkey: I don't know.
Mrs. Turkey: Remind me never to send you to the
   store for lemons!

If a turkey was born in Virginia, raised in Mississippi,
and died in Louisiana, what is it?
Dead.

**Turkey:** Where are you taking me?
**Farmer:** I'm taking you home for dinner.
**Turkey:** I've already had dinner. Take me to a movie.

**Steve Cow:** I heard Nick Turkey swallowed a
quarter. How is he?
**Chris Turkey:** No change yet.